THE PLASTER MOLD CASTING HANDBOOK

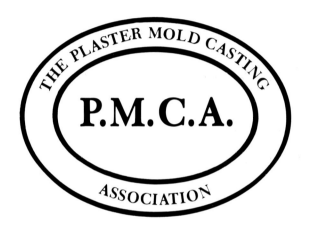

1983

THE PLASTER MOLD CASTING HANDBOOK

Published by The Plaster Mold Casting Association.

Editorial Director: Anthony M. Arcesi

PLASTER MOLD CASTING HANDBOOK

The Plaster Mold Casting Handbook has been published to provide a description of the plaster mold casting process and its applications; its unique benefits and advantages; design parameters and considerations; and examples of typical performance.

It represents the cumulative experience and expertise of the Plaster Mold Casting Association membership.

PREFACE

The primary purpose of this Handbook is to provide the designers and purchasers of precision castings with a complete reference source for the plaster mold casting process. This text provides all of the basic information needed to intelligently design a plaster mold casting.

Included in the text is a section on alloys cast with the process, as well as specific design information on tolerances, wall thickness, and surface finish.

Numerous examples of typical performance are shown to illustrate how designers have taken advantage of the process to build precision metal castings at the lowest possible cost.

The text also contains a complete section on the special use of the plaster mold process to build "cast-to-size" tooling, as utilized in the sandcasting industry, as well as the plastics and packaging industries.

I thank the members of the Plaster Mold Casting Association for their cooperation and support in helping to make the development and production of this text possible.

Anthony M. Arcesi
Vice-President
Atlantic Casting & Engineering Corporation

Air diffuser casting, 48″ diameter x 15″ deep, over 225 lbs. Aluminum alloy 356-T6. Courtesy Atlantic Casting and Engineering Corp.

TABLE OF CONTENTS

THE PLASTER MOLD CASTING PROCESS

INTRODUCTION

Originally developed by the bronze statuary casters of medieval times, and limited in its application for many subsequent years, the plaster mold casting process is now one of the most important casting techniques in the United States. Advances in mold material development and other technical areas have keyed increased acceptance.

Virtually all the plaster mold foundries in the world are located in the United States. Castings from these domestic producers are commonly sold to the European market, as designers worldwide seek to take increasing advantage of the unique benefits offered by the plaster mold casting process.

After the permanent-mold, die-, and sand-casting processes, the plaster mold casting process is probably the most widely used casting technique in the United States for aluminum- and copper-base foundry products. The development of the permeable plasters used in the *rubber pattern plaster mold process*, and the refinement of the solid plasters used in the *rigid pattern plaster mold process*, have together keyed significant growth in applications for the process in recent years.

Although the plaster mold process is not considered directly competitive with the permanent-mold, sand-casting, or die-casting processes, it is regarded as a technique that can yield castings not obtainable through those other processes. On the other hand, plaster mold castings are very competitive when compared to investment castings, especially for larger castings made from aluminum- or copper-base alloys.

Because of mold material strength considerations, only castings made from aluminum-, zinc-, or copper-base alloys can be produced by the plaster mold process.

However, plaster mold castings can be produced in quantities

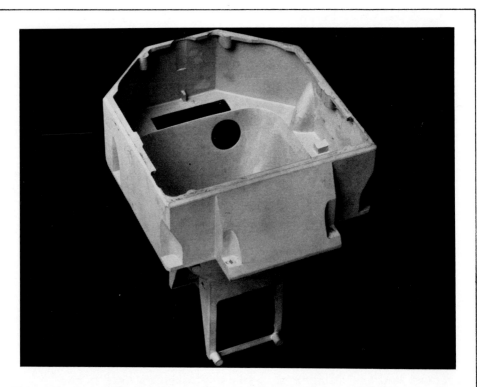

Thin-wall electronics housing, with extensive undercuts. Casting measures 11″ x 15″ x 10″, with 0.06″ thick walls throughout. Aluminum, A356-T6.

of one piece to several thousand, and in sizes ranging from one ounce to one ton. They are noted for their fine surface finish, highly accurate pattern detail reproduction, consistently close tolerances, and uniform hardness and dimensional stability.

In addition, the slow metal solidification rate caused by the almost "insulating" nature of the dehydrated plaster mold material results in minimum warpage or distortion, as well as very low levels of cast-in internal stresses. This significant feature can greatly reduce the time and cost required for subsequent straightening or machining operations.

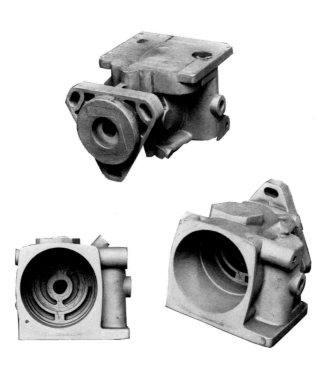

Plaster mold casting used as a prototype die casting: a diesel fuel pump housing for European automotive use. Aluminum alloy 356-T6; 10″ x 6″ x 6″.

Aluminum- and copper-base alloy castings with thin sections are routinely cast, while parts requiring complex and intricate coring are also readily produced. Reproduction of fine surface detail, one of the more easily recognized benefits offered by the process, is excellent in plaster mold castings.

Plaster mold castings made from aluminum, zinc, and copper alloys often serve as prototypes for testing new design engineering ideas, thereby contributing significantly to new-product development programs.

Often used as prototype diecastings, plaster-cast parts closely simulate both the dimensional accuracy and the surface finish available through the conventional diecasting process. Since tooling time and other costs required to build a plaster mold casting is usually one-tenth (1/10) that needed for conventional die casting tooling, designers can "prove out" a concept without risking long delays and high costs.

Innovative sales and marketing ideas can be tested in the same manner, with inexpensive plaster mold castings limiting initial costs, and also limiting costs needed to provide design updates.

As described in Section IV, the plaster mold casting process is also used to produce cast-to-size tooling, including both matchplate castings for sand casting foundries and mold castings for the plastics industry.

PROCESS DESCRIPTION

Summary

The plaster mold casting process is a split-pattern technique that is similar to the common sand-casting process. The primary differences between the two processes are that plaster mold patterns are accurately machined from metallic or acryllic materials as opposed to being fabricated from wood, and also use a plaster slurry as mold material instead of sand. As a result, the dimensional accuracies and surface finishes that are typically obtained are significantly superior to those realized through sand casting.

Tooling consists of a permanent pattern machined into two parts. The casting shape is divided along a parting line that is established to provide the best tolerance advantage with no undercuts in either half. If undercut portions are needed, cores are produced separately in precision-built core boxes and placed in the mold halves to form any undercuts.

In a specialized, cost-effective technique known as the Capaco Process, or "strip method", groups of pattern halves for many different parts are mounted in separate flasks and locked into position. This shared-mold concept allows for extremely cost-effective production of small parts and/or short runs because the costs for mold production are shared proportionately by all of the different castings in the mold. When an order for one particular casting is completed, its pattern is removed and immediately replaced with another.

Plaster molds are made by mixing a metalcasting plaster, other refractory materials, and water to form a slurry. The slurry is then poured over the patterns and sets firm within five to fifteen minutes.

Prior to slurry pouring, a mold parting compound is applied to the patterns, in order to help provide for subsequent easy release of the plaster mold from the pattern. Because of the fine surface finish of the pattern, and the smooth finish of the set plaster, a minimum of molding draft is required on the pattern. This lack of draft is one of the major design benefits gained with plaster mold castings.

When the plaster mold halves have been drawn from the patterns, they are placed in drying ovens, where both free and chemically-bonded water molecules are driven off. Molds may be dried in batch-type ovens, or in conveyorized ovens that have been programmed to remove water at a precise rate to assure complete drying without thermal shock. Cores are dried in a similar manner, usually at the same time as their parent molds.

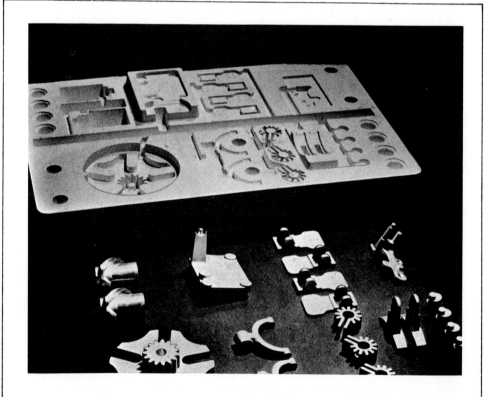

4) A typical plaster mold half, showing 20 castings produced for nine customers.

Mold drying is one of the most critical steps in plaster mold casting production, because complete removal of all moisture is necessary to prevent the outgassing of steam when molten metal is introduced into the mold. A drying cycle of 500 °F for 12-16 hours is normally used for plaster molds that will receive aluminum or zinc alloys. When copper-base alloys are to be cast, the molds are usually dried at 1300-1500 °F.

The higher drying temperature for copper-base casting is necessary to assure elimination of all moisture before casting that takes place at temperatures about one and a half times higher than those used for aluminum or zinc alloys. The possibility of steam outgassing is greatly increased in copper-base casting, and molds must be more thoroughly dried to assure metallurgically sound castings.

When the dried halves are removed from the ovens, any cores, chills, or inserts required are placed in them, and the halves are precisely doweled together.

The assembled mold is then clamped into a fixture for pouring. Pouring may be performed entirely in a vacuum, with a vacuum-assist through one half of the mold, with an induced pressure, or with gravity assist only. Selection of the particular pouring method will depend on the foundry's equipment capabilities and/or the metallurgical requirements of the final product.

The insulating properties of the dried plaster mold material keep the metal from solidifying long enough to allow for filling of the thinnest sections, while the inherent permeability of the mold material permits escape of mold gases if required. Furthermore, the relatively long solidification time associated with plaster molds allows for the time needed to effectively accomplished any vacuum-assist as described above.

After cooling, molds are carefully broken away from the castings, and gates and risers are removed.

Finishing of the castings is accomplished by removing the parting lines, and either abrasive-blasting or acid-etching the parts prior to shipment.

Metal Casting Plasters

Different plaster formulations are used for the *rigid pattern* and *rubber pattern* plaster mold processes. However, the fundamental ingredient in either case is the mineral commonly called Plaster of Paris ($CaSO_4 \cdot 1 \cdot 5H_2O$). Gypsum and additives of various other compounds are blended in order to control set time, green mold strength, fired strength, and mold shrinkage.

When the gypsum is mixed with water, it reacts chemically to form a slurry of $CaSO_4 \cdot 2H_2O$. At this point, the mold has sufficient strength to be extracted from the pattern. After proper drying, the waters of hydration have been removed in a two-step process, and anhydrous calcium sulfate ($CaSO_4$) remains. A temperature of 220 °F is required throughout the mold to achieve the complete dehydration process.

Conventional metalcasting plaster mixes are used in the *rigid pattern* plaster mold process. These mixes are excellent for yielding dimensional accuracy, good surface finish, and intricate detail, but they have relatively low permeability, which develops from their gypsum bond. Thus, it is very common for rigid pattern plaster mold producers to use a complete or partial vacuum assist during the pouring operation as an aid to effective filling and mold gas removal.

Molds made from permeable plaster are used in the *rubber pattern* plaster mold process in order to minimize venting problems. These permeable metalcasting plasters are made primarily from gypsum and other main ingredients, but they also have a foaming additive. During mixing, the foaming additive causes a porous structure of small, uniform, interconnected cells to form just under a smooth surface. When the mold is dried, these interconnected passages offer a natural path through which mold gases may escape during the metal casting operation.

Although the mold drying operation is not as critical here as it is with conventional plaster, the mixing and mold-making steps are considerably more difficult. This is because the size, number, and distribution of the cells is very important to the achievement of the natural venting structure of the dried mold.

Pattern Equipment

Pattern equipment used for the *rigid pattern* plaster mold casting technique is completely different than that used for the *rubber pattern* method, with the equipment usually not interchangeable.

Because of the cellular structure in permeable metalcasting plasters, extraction from a rigid pattern with minimum draft is difficult. The very thin surface of the plaster has minimum mechanical strength, and cannot withstand the normal forces that occur with the extraction of a rigid pattern from the mold. Thus, flexible rubber patterns, which can be easily deformed to allow effective withdrawal from the mold, are used instead. Traditionally, a polysulfide or "Black Tuffy" type of rubber was used for the patterns. This type of rubber pattern has a limited service life and must be replaced when the rub-- ber loses its original form. However, replacement rubber can be cast off master patterns from which the original rubber was cast, and plaster mold production can continue.

With recent developments in urethane technology, several *rubber pattern* plaster mold foundries now make their flexible patterns from urethane material. Modern urethane materials are much tougher and more durable than the polysulfide rubbers, and patterns made from urethane do not need to be replaced very frequently. In fact, the urethane pattern can offer an extended service life approaching that normally associated with rigid plaster mold toolings.

Patterns used with the *rigid pattern* plaster mold process are machined directly from metallic or acrylic materials, and must be regarded as permanent structures. For very limited production runs, wood patterns may be used, but they must be very carefully sealed to prevent the absorption of water from the plaster slurry.

Rigid patterns must have some draft allowance, even though it may be as little as ¼°, to assist in extracting the plaster mold from the pattern. Pattern-making techniques common to other foundry processes are used to produce patterns for the rigid plaster mold process, so long as they allow for extreme precision, minimum draft, and very fine surface finish.

Parting Compounds

Regardless of the type of pattern equipment or plaster used, it is always necessary to apply some type of release agent to the patterns before pouring the plaster slurry, thereby facilitating pattern removal later. Each foundry may have its own special parting agent, but they all usually consist of some type of wax or oil in a petrochemical vehicle that allows for application of a thin coat. Heavy greases and plastic compounds are not used because they tend to soften the mold surface, resulting in loss of detail reproduction.

Slurry Mixing and Pouring, Rigid Pattern

With conventional metalcasting plasters used during the rigid pattern plaster mold casting process, the water-to-plaster ratio is of primary importance. A carefully weighed portion of plaster mix should be added to a carefully weighed portion of water, and mixed to obtain a creamy consistency.

Consistency is defined as the ratio, by weight, of water to

powder (plaster). Thus, a ratio of 140 lbs. of water to 100 lbs. of plaster mix powder is recorded as a consistency of 1.4. Changes in the consistency have a significant effect on the final plaster mold product. Examples of the impact of increases in consistency are as follows:

1) Fired strength is decreased.
2) Permeability of dried mold is increased.
3) Mold shrinkage is increased.
4) Unfired (green) strength is decreased.

The setting time for the plaster slurry can be reduced by increasing the water temperature, changing the speed or shape of the mixer to increase mixing energy, or by the use of chemical additives.

After the proper proportions of water and plaster have been thoroughly mixed, the resultant slurry is promptly and gently poured over the pattern(s). (Patterns, of course, have been previously coated with an appropriate parting agent.) Prior to setting, it is frequently necessary to shake or vibrate the molding table to prevent air bubbles and trapped air pockets from forming next to the pattern.

After the plaster slurry has set, the mold may be extracted from the pattern. The most common method of extraction is to mechanically lift the mold off the pattern. Frequently, a small wire is pushed through the mold, and air is subsequently introduced to assist with separating the mold. The pattern remains on the mold table while the mold is sent to the drying oven.

Slurry Mixing and Pouring, Rubber Pattern

Since the success of the rubber-pattern plaster mold process is impacted heavily by the quality of the surface and structure of the mold, proper plaster mixing and pouring operations are critical.

As is the case with conventional plasters, the proper proportion of water to plaster powder mix is important, but the particularly vital operation is the mixing cycle. Consistencies of one-to-one are most common and are normally sufficient. Air must be incorporated during the mixing cycle to increase the volume by 70-100% from the original.

In order to achieve the ideal structure of a smooth surface and a cellular base, the mixing procedure must be designed to produce uniform density and permeability, while maintaining a strong surface. Proper mixing of the water, air, and plaster powder require good temperature control of the powder and water, as well as effective control of mixing time, mixing speed, and the volume of the slurry.

A mixing device which beats air into the mixture to produce a uniform cell size of approximately 0.01″ in diameter is ideal. Larger cell sizes reduce the surface layer strength, while smaller cell sizes can greatly reduce mold permeability.

Variations in the water-to-plaster ratio do not have as great an effect on final mold size as they do with conventional plasters. The amount of air blended into the slurry has a greater effect, so careful attention must be paid to mixer speed, mixer size and configuration, bucket size, and slurry volume.

The mixed slurry is then promptly poured over the flexible patterns, which have been previously coated with a parting agent. Gentle brushing or vibration of the mold table is performed to avoid entrapped air, and to cause the larger bubbles to move off the surface of the pattern.

After the plaster slurry has set, the mold is lifted off the mold table. The flexible pattern usually has begun to lift off its support. allowing for "peeling" out of the plaster mold. The rubber pattern is re-inserted over the pattern support remaining on the mold table, preparing for the beginning of another molding cycle.

Plaster Mold Drying

The self-supporting plaster mold halves are loaded into drying ovens, where the free and chemically-bonded water will be removed. Regardless of the type of plaster used, all of the water must be removed before metal may be successfully cast in the mold. Also, the molds must be supported during drying to avoid cracking or warping.

When copper-base alloys are to be cast, the mold must be dried above 1200 °F to assure complete dehydration. The type of oven equipment utilized will vary, but high-temperature drying will require that the temperature be cycled in order to prevent chemical decomposition and cracking of the surface layers. If overheated, the surface layers will decompose, and the mold will exhibit excessive dimensional shrinkage.

The lower drying temperatures associated with production of aluminum and zinc plaster mold castings mean that mold overheating is not the problem it is during the high-temperature drying cycles needed for copper-base plaster mold casting.

Equally important to stable mold production is the cooling cycle. If the calcined mold is rapidly cooled, thermal shock will cause mold cracking. Cooling time at various temperature levels should also be closely controlled, and is usually done via automatic control devices.

In lower-temperature drying performed during the production of aluminum or zinc castings, the molds are baked at temperatures ranging from 400-500 °F. Common practices used to determine when complete calcination has occurred are either the loss-of-weight technique, or a thermocouple reading in excess of 220 °F measured at the center of the mold.

Since drying operations involve both time and temperature phenomena, actual drying times may vary from mold to mold. Some of the factors that influence drying time are mold surface area, mold thickness, mold permeability, capacity of the heat input source, and the circulation efficiency of the oven.

Cores are normally dried alongside their parent molds. Because some cores are very delicate, it is common to use specialized core drying forms to provide for uniform support of the plaster cores during the dehydration process.

Special care must be exercised to prevent re-hydration of all calcined plaster molds prior to casting. Since it is the nature of calcined plaster to absorb moisture from the atmosphere, special precautions must be observed if calcined molds are to be stored overnight. Most calcined molds are poured immediately after removal from the oven in order to avoid this problem of partial re-hydration.

Calcined plaster molds are removed from the oven when they are at about 120-150 °F, and any cores, chills, or inserts are immediately assembled into the mold halves. The molds are then clamped and poured.

Plaster molds can only be used once, and the spent plaster cannot be economically recycled. At this time, research is being conducted on economical ways of recycling the plaster, and in the future such recycling may very well become a reality.

Gating and Pouring

The insulating properties of calcined plaster molds offer several advantages, and also present some difficulties, when the plaster mold foundryman performs gating and pouring.

With copper-base alloys, the solidification rate allows for smaller gates and risers than is the case in sandcasting. This translates into sounder castings and lower costs because of more efficient mold space utilization, and also higher metal yields. (Metal yield is defined as pounds of castings produced divided by pounds of metal poured.)

With aluminum-base alloys, the plaster mold allows for the casting of intricate sections, but the slow solidification rate allows time for gas pickup from the mold. In order to produce radiographically sound castings, it is usually necessary to establish strong directional solidification paths through the use of chills, and to use vacuum assist to vent the mold gases away from the molten metal. One of the distinct advantages of the permeable plaster mold process is the natural permeability that occurs through the cellular structure of the mold.

Standard, unpressurized gating systems are used in the process to produce high-integrity castings that are suitable for both industrial and aerospace applications.

Finishing

Shakeout with plaster mold castings is much easier than it is with sand or investment castings because of the relatively low strength of the calcined molds. Gates, risers, and parting lines are easily trimmed, and finished castings are frequently used with a minimum requirement of secondary machining or finishing operations.

BENEFITS AND ADVANTAGES

Highly Diverse Applicability

There are virtually no restrictions on shapes that can be made via plaster mold casting techniques. In addition, the process is not limited to low unit weights, or to low unit runs. Production quantities of 100,000 can be readily achieved through duplication of required patterns from a master.

As described in the case history section of this book ("Proven Performance With Plaster Mold Castings"), the process can be used for casting a wide variety of aluminum-base and copper-base alloys, with zinc-base types also applicable.

The process has also gained popularity as a means for producing diecasting prototypes without investing heavily in die tooling costs and time. It has been employed similarly to test new design or marketing ideas, regardless of the casting process eventually chosen for full production.

With the increasing use of structural foam and other types of plastic part production, designers are also using plaster mold castings as a method for prototyping parts to save time and tooling development costs, even though volume production may be performed with a petrochemical material.

With the inherent cost advantage plaster mold castings have over investment castings, designers of large aerospace parts are able to achieve considerable savings by taking advantage of the versatility of the plaster mold casting process without sacrificing material integrity or dimensional accuracy.

Exceptional Qualitative Control

Since plaster mold materials commonly employed provide for a relatively high degree of insulation, solidification time is lengthened considerably compared to other casting methods. This provides for excellent filling of thin and intricate sections, while minimizing internal stresses in the finished casting.

Surface quality of plaster mold castings is regarded as the best obtainable from any casting method. Frequently, no further machining or finishing operations are required. Exceptional, uniform smoothness is readily attainable. When desired, consistent stylized surface types can be achieved, surpassing even those gained through other molding methods. In addition, highly accurate reproduction of special details is routinely accomplished.

Holes and cutouts of any shape may be incorporated with minimum restriction, while fillets and corner radii can be made from sharp to any full radius.

Competitive Quantitative Control

Surface accuracy and various dimensional tolerances approximate those obtainable through die- and investment casting. Designers are advised to refer to Section II for a discussion of the major tolerance parameters. Highlights are as follows:

Surface Accuracy
90-125 RMS (Root Mean Square); C60 maximum on Visual Surface Comparator Sample Chart.

Linear Tolerances
General: ± 0.005 in./in. from 0-6 in.; ± 0.003 in./in. thereafter, with maximum tolerance of ± 0.040 in./in.

Parting Line Tolerances
In the split pattern molding process commonly used, the normal rule for tolerances which go to or across any parting line is ± 0.015 in.

Draft Requirements
Normal, ½°−2°/in. of draw; premium, 0−¼°/in. of draw. Draft-free condition via use of core in rigid pattern plaster mold process; draft-free mold sections using the rubber

pattern plaster mold process.

Holes and Cutouts
Minimum ¼ in. diameter.

Angles
0° to ± ½° maximum tolerance range.

Perpendicularity
Normal: 0.008 in. per in. of length of shorter plane.
Premium: 0.005 in. per in. of length of shorter plane.

Wall Thickness
Normal tolerance: ± 0.015 in.
Premium tolerance: ± 0.010 in.
Typically obtainable wall thicknesses:
  Aluminum-base alloys: 0.070 in. normal; 0.040 in. premium.
  Copper-base alloys: 0.090 in. normal; 0.040 in. premium.
  Zinc-base alloys: 0.060 in. normal; 0.040 in. premium.

Typical Machine Stock Allowances
Surfaces: 0.030-0.060 in.
Cast Holes: 0.015-0.060 in.

Cost-Effective Production

Tooling costs for plaster mold casting are usually greater than that for a sand casting, similar to those for an investment casting, and less than those for permanent mold or die casting.

Sample casting lead times are comparable to those for sand casting, and are usually much less than those for investment or die castings. Two to six weeks from order to delivery is common.

Plaster mold casting allows for particularly cost-effective mold production. Patterns for a group of different castings can share the same flask, dividing mold production cost among a number of jobs. Since there is little, if any, wear on patterns during the process, they rarely require replacement before full production is completed. Also, plaster mold patterns can be easily and quickly changed to accommodate design revisions.

Slow metal solidification that is characteristic of plaster mold casting reduces eventual total production costs by alleviating stress concentration, promoting uniform hardness, providing for accurate control of shrinkage, and resulting in negligible warping.

DESIGNING FOR PLASTER MOLD CASTING

GENERAL CONSIDERATIONS

Introduction

General considerations and principles established for all casting design efforts apply to the plaster mold process. Foremost among these is the need for close cooperation between casting designer and casting producer as early as possible in the design process, and well ahead of design finalization. This principle has gained increasing acceptance in many different engineering disciplines in recent years, as a means for assuring optimum realization of manufacturing process advantages, at the lowest cost, in the shortest time.

Good casting design practice incorporates two basic objectives. The first is to effectively meet functional end-use requirements, including workable interface with adjacent components. The second is to provide for cost-effective casting production, including maximizing metal usage and ease of casting while minimizing secondary operations — all at the lowest cost and within the shortest time.

Accomplishing these objectives requires careful evaluation of a number of basic considerations and parameters. These include choosing between casting a job as a unit, or casting it as components for later joining via a selected joining method; establishing methods for molding, coring, and pattern construction; positioning of gates, risers, and chills; defining alloy composition; providing for alloy solidification time and direction; designing section thicknesses, tapers, fillets, and configurations to achieve strength and intricacy while limiting mass; establishing pouring practice, heat treatment procedure, and tolerance requirements; determining casting weight, shape, reinforcement technique, and control of compression, bending, tension, and torsion stresses; and other considerations as required.

Well-documented foundry engineering principles apply to all of these general considerations and parameters, but rigid rules are no substitute for cooperative communication between the designer and the producer. Those designers who are not well-grounded in foundry engineering should not hesitate to contact a plaster mold casting supplier for assistance.

The versatility of the plaster mold process allows for the production of virtually any casting size or shape. However, designers using this process must still observe the rules for sound and practical design if they are to avoid unnecessary costs.

Tooling Points and Datum Planes

One of the first steps in drawing any casting should be the incorporation of the datum plane method of dimensioning, and definition of a tooling point system. Use of the datum plane technique will usually help to minimize tooling and casting costs because interpretation of drawings will be much simpler, while fixtures will be less costly. Datum plane dimensioning also facilitates casting inspection, and assures consistency of inspection results between casting suppliers and casting users.

Tooling points should be used to establish three datum planes, and should be located whenever possible on the same side of the parting line in order to reduce variations caused by mold mismatch. In addition, the tooling points should be located such that they will not be affected by gate or parting line removal. See Figure #1.

Finally, tooling points should be located as far apart as the shape of the part permits, and preferably should be coincident with the basic datum planes.

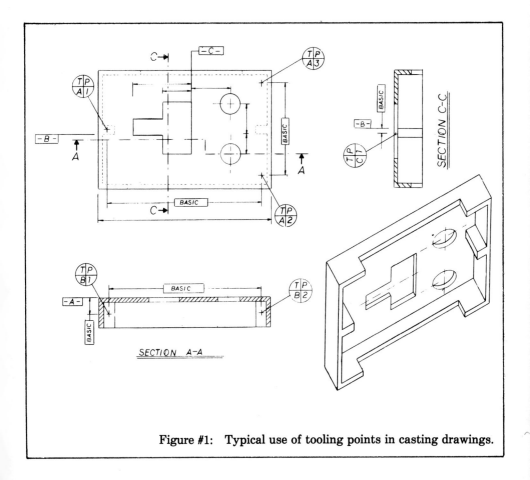

Figure #1: Typical use of tooling points in casting drawings.

Section Thickness

Although the plaster mold process allows for the casting of almost any shape or size, the casting designer should give consideration to providing uniform material thickness whenever possible. Regardless of the casting process selected, the foundry must establish a sequence of metal solidification within the casting that compensates for changes in section thickness, in order to help assure a dense, sound casting. Obviously, not all parts can be designed with a completely uniform cross-sectional thickness, but efforts should be made to avoid abrupt transitions from thick to thin sections.

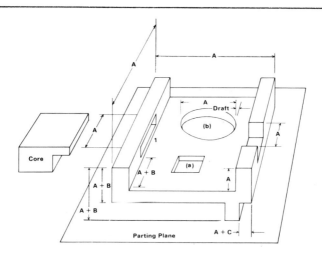

Figure #2:

Parting lines and casting dimensions:

"A" Dimensions: any dimension contained completely within one mold half or within a core.

"B" Dimensions: additional tolerance required to compensate for closeover of plaster mold halves at the parting line, or for hand positioning of cores.

"C" Dimensions: subject to possible mismatch or shift when mold halves are assembled.

Where "B" and "C" tolerances affect critical dimensions adversely, they can often be eliminated by relocation of the parting plane.

When such transitions are unavoidable, it is advisable to gradually increase the section size from thin to thick sections. Use of generous fillets and corner radii are excellent examples of blending abrupt changes in section size or geometry.

Mold and Core Parting Planes

The intelligent selection of mold and core parting planes is critical to realizing the maximum economic benefits available through the plaster mold casting process. The split-pattern concept that is basic to the process means each casting will have a parting line, and there is a tolerance buildup across every parting line. This results from the joining of the calcined mold halves to one another.

If possible, it is advisable to consult a plaster mold casting supplier early in the design stage to discuss parting line selection, since the parting line can frequently be located in such a way that it will not affect a close tolerance area of the casting. Figure #2 shows how dimensions are affected by the parting line in a typical plaster mold casting.

Standards for Performance

Mechanical properties obtainable from plaster mold castings rival those realized from other precision casting processes. Plaster mold castings are routinely produced to satisfy specifications of the Aluminum Association, the American Society for Testing and Materials (ASTM), and various Federal, aerospace, and military standards.

The casting designer should explicitly specify desired strength levels based on functional performance requirements, and clearly communicate those requirements to the casting supplier. Normal tension testing and hardness testing techniques are used to determine mechanical property values.

The level of casting integrity required for the casting users' application should be clearly specified directly on the engineering drawing. The most common method of specification is reference to Mil C 6021 for nondestructive inspection. By properly specifying the class and grade per Mil C 6021, the designer can effectively explain the required casting integrity and required testing to the casting supplier.

Routine fluorescent penetrant and radiographic inspection techniques can be used to assure the plaster mold casting quality that is necessary for many sophisticated applications.

Careful consideration should be given to permitting weld repair of minor casting defects, because of the potentially significant impact on final casting costs. In addition, stress levels experienced by the end-use casting must be thoroughly researched, along with mechanical strength levels available in professionally weld-repaired areas. In most cases, properly weld-repaired areas will possess better mechanical properties than the base casting material.

DESIGN PARAMETERS AND TOLERANCES

Introduction

Dimensional and tolerance standards for plaster mold castings are detailed in this sub-section. These tolerances are generally accepted throughout the industry, but it is recommended that you discuss your particular requirements with your plaster mold casting supplier. Premium tolerances are possible, but usually result in increased manufacturing costs.

Tolerance Standards for Plaster Mold Castings

1. **Linear Tolerances**
    a) As a general rule the linear tolerance on a plaster mold casting will be determined as follows:
        $\pm$ .005 in./in. from 0-6 inches.
        $\pm$ .003 in./in. thereafter with a maximum tolerance of $\pm$ .040 in.

    b) Normal casting tolerances are those tolerances which can be achieved in the plaster mold process on a repetitive basis from one production run to another. (Refer to Chart I)

    c) Premium casting tolerances can be achieved in the plaster mold process but they will require added operations and thus involve additional costs. It should be emphasized that premium tolerances can only be maintained on a few *selected dimensions* of a casting and that specification of a premium tolerance should be discussed with your plaster mold casting supplier. (Refer to Chart I for a listing of obtainable premium tolerances.)

2. **Parting Line Tolerances;**
    a) The plaster mold process is a split pattern molding process and requires a cope mold to drag mold parting line and, on occasion, a core to mold parting lines. The

normal rule for tolerances on dimensions which go to
or across any parting line is +.015 ".

CHART I
PLASTER MOLD CASTING TOLERANCES

DIMENSION		NORMAL TOLERANCE		PREMIUM TOLERANCE	
Inches	MM	Inches	MM	Inches	MM
Up to 2	Up to 50	±.010	± .25	±.005	±.13
Up to 3	Up to 75	±.015	± .40	±.010	±.25
Up to 4	Up to 100	±.019	± .50	±.012	±.32
Up to 5	Up to 125	±.022	± .60	±.014	±.37
Up to 6	Up to 150	±.025	± .68	±.015	±.40
Up to 7	Up to 175	±.028	± .74	±.016	±.42
Up to 8	Up to 200	±.031	± .78	±.017	±.45
Up to 9	Up to 225	±.034	± .85	±.018	±.47
Up to 10	Up to 250	±.037	± .92	±.019	±.50
Maximum Variation		±.040	±1.00	—	—

b) If a premium parting line tolerance is required, a
+.010 " tolerance can be achieved, but as with any
premium tolerance, the designer should bear in mind
that extra operations will be required to hold the
premium tolerance and that the premium tolerance
will increase the cost of the casting. Close cooperation
with your casting supplier at the early stages of
design on the selection of the parting line(s) can often
times prevent the need to use premium tolerances.

3. **Draft Requirements:**
   a) In order to extract the plaster mold from a rigid pattern, some draft is required. With standard engineering drawing practice draft will add mass to the dimension. Any desired exception to this practice should be clearly defined on the drawing. Again, close cooperation with your plaster mold casting supplier can be very useful in establishing the draft requirements of a particular part. (Refer to Chart II)

   b) Because of the flexibility of the rubber mold, draft is seldom required when utilizing the rubber pattern plaster mold process.

CHART II
DRAFT REQUIREMENTS

NORMAL	PREMIUM
½° to 2° per inch of draw	0 to ¼° per inch of draw

   c) The rigid pattern plaster mold process can provide for a draft free condition by the use of a core. The designer should discuss his specific requirements with his plaster mold casting supplier in order to get the maximum advantages from the casting process.

4. **Holes and Cutouts:**
   Holes and cutouts of any shape can be obtained in a plaster mold process with a minimum of restrictions. The major constraint is that the minimum hole or cutout size is a ¼" diameter.

5. **Cast Surface Texture:**
   a) Common industrial practice is to specify surface finish in one of the following terms:
   1. RMS (Root Mean Square)
   2. Visual Surface Comparator Sample.
   The latter method is gaining wide approval, and it is the preferred method for all forms of casting. Specifically, the plaster mold process can produce castings with surface finishes ranging from 90 to 125 RMS or C60 maximum on the visual comparator chart.

6. **Angles:**
   Angles may be specified with a tolerance range of 0° to ±½° maximum.

7. **Perpendicularity:**
   a) The designer should use caution in specifying the perpendicularity tolerance, and it is very advisable that he should discuss the subject with the plaster mold casting supplier before finalizing the drawing tolerance.

   b) Perpendicularity is best specified as the relation of a reference plane to another plane. The longer of the two planes involved should be called out as the reference plane and the tolerance applied to the other plane. (Refer to Chart III)

CHART III
PERPENDICULARITY TOLERANCES

NORMAL	PREMIUM
.008" per inch of length of the shorter plane	.005" per inch of length of the shorter plane

8. **Straightness and Flatness;**
   a) These parameters are often confused and a definite understanding of what is required must be determined between the designer and the casting supplier.
      1. Flatness tolerance. It relates that the total deviation of one entire surface from a parallel plane separated by some distance must be equal to the tolerance specified. The tolerance is measured from a single reference plane. Generalized tolerance rules for normal or premium tolerance requirements would not be realistic since flatness tolerance is dependent on the particular design configuration and alloy. As is the case with other important design parameters, the designer should discuss his requirements with his plaster mold casting supplier at the earliest design stage possible. The following chart lists some design guidelines on flatness of plaster mold castings:

CHART IV
FLATNESS

FLATNESS AREA (Square Inches)	TYPICAL STRAIGHTNESS TOLERANCE (TIR)
4	.010"
16	.015"
36	.025"

      2. Straightness tolerance. It relates that all points along a *single surface* must lie within a specified tolerance zone measured from the theoretical axis of the surface.

a) As with flatness, a general tolerance rule for straightness is not possible, and specific requirements should be discussed between the designer and his plaster mold casting supplier.

b) Straightness tolerance is controlled by a supplier's ability to mechanically straighten a casting, and listed below in Chart V are some design guidelines. (Specific tolerances should be discussed with the casting supplier.)

CHART V
STRAIGHTNESS REQUIREMENTS

LENGTH OF SURFACE (Inches)	TYPICAL STRAIGHTNESS TOLERANCE (TIR)
0-2	.008″
2-6	.015″
6-10	.025″
10-15	.030″
15-20	.045″
over 20	.060″

9. **Fillets and Corner Radii:**
   a) Cast outside corners — sharp to any full radius.

   b) Fillet radii — sharp to any full radius.

10. **Wall Thickness Tolerance:**
    a) Normal tolerance is ±.015.″

    b) Premium tolerance is ±.010.″

11. Machine Stock Allowance:

a) Areas requiring extra material for machining should be *clearly* defined on the drawing. Typical machine stock allowances in surfaces range from .030 to .060 inches, and for cast holes ranges from .015" to .060". Use of the .015" stock allowance for cast holes should occur only when the anticipated machining procedure and final product usage allows use of the *cast hole location.*

12. Minimum Wall Thickness:

The castable wall thickness depends upon the design configuration and alloy used. Listed in Chart VI are some typically obtainable wall thicknesses using the plaster mold casting technique.

CHART VI
WALL THICKNESS

	NORMAL	PREMIUM
Aluminum Based Alloys	.070"	.040"
Copper Based Alloys	.090"	.040"
Zinc Based Alloys	.060"	.040"

SELECTION OF ALLOYS FOR THE PLASTER MOLD CASTING PROCESS

GENERAL CONSIDERATIONS

Primary criteria in alloy selection for plaster mold casting are mechanical properties.

Mechanical properties may be determined from either separately-cast test specimens, or from test specimens machined from various sections of a casting. The level of obtainable mechanical properties will vary, depending on the location from which test specimens are selected.

A complete understanding between casting supplier and casting user on how test specimens are to be selected is essential. This subject should be negotiated with your plaster mold casting supplier before production commences.

ALUMINUM-BASE PLASTER MOLD CASTING ALLOYS

Properties and characteristics of some of the aluminum-base alloys most frequently cast in plaster molds are shown in the following table. Of the alloys and tempers listed, the A356 alloy is most commonly specified. The −T51 temper is normally specified for simulated die casting applications, while the −T6 temper is used for more demanding engineering applications. In special cases, a −T71 temper can be called out if exceptional dimensional stability after machining is required.

TABLE 1: MECHANICAL PROPERTIES, ALUMINUM-BASE ALLOYS

Alloy	Class	Temper	Tensile Strength, Minimum (p.s.i.)	Yield Str., 0.2% offset min. (p.s.i.)	%Elongation in 0.2″, min.
319	—	AC	23,000	15,000	1.5
C355		−T6	36,000	25,000	1.0
	10*	−T6	41,000	31,000	3.0
	11*	−T6	37,000	30,000	1.0
	12*	−T6	35,000	28,000	1.0
A356		−T51	25,000	20,000	1.5
		−T6	30,000	20,000	2.0
		−T71	30,000	25,000	1.0
	10*	−T6	38,000	28,000	5.0
	11*	−T6	33,000	27,000	3.0
	12*	−T6	32,000	22,000	2.0
A357	10*	−T6	38,000	28,000	5.0
	11*	−T6	41,000	31,000	3.0
713		−T5	32,000	22,000	3.0

*Values from Mil A 21180C, "Aluminum Alloy Castings-High Strength". The above values are provided for reference only — not for design. Specific mechanical properties must be negotiated with the plaster mold casting foundry.

TABLE 2: CHEMICAL COMPOSITION, ALUMINUM-BASE ALLOYS

	Alloy 319	Alloy C355*	Alloy A356**	Alloy A357***	Alloy 713****
Copper	3.0-4.0	1.0-1.5	0.10	0.10	0.40-1.0
Silicon	5.5-6.5	4.5-5.5	6.5-7.5	6.5-7.5	0.25
Iron	0.6	0.13	0.11	0.12	0.80
Manganese	0.10	0.05	0.05	0.05	0.60
Zinc	0.10	0.05	0.05	0.05	7.0-8.0
Magnesium	0.10	0.50-0.60	0.30-0.40	0.45-0.70	0.25-0.50
Titanium	0.20	0.20	0.20	0.10-0.20	0.25
Others, each	—	0.05	0.05	0.03	0.10
Others, total	0.20	0.15	0.15	0.10	0.25
Aluminum	rmdr.	rmdr.	rmdr.	rmdr.	rmdr.

*Alloy C355 exhibits good corrosion resistance and very good retention of as-cast or heat-treated mechanical properties at elevated temperatures up to 300°F.

**Alloy A356 exhibits good corrosion resistance, good pressure tightness, and good weldability.

***Alloy A357 contains 0.04-0.07% beryllium, and exhibits good pressure tightness and good corrosion resistance.

****Alloy 713 exhibits good corrosion resistance, excellent anodizing properties, and is brazeable. This alloy is self-aging.

ZINC-BASE PLASTER MOLD CASTING ALLOY

TABLE 3: MECHANICAL PROPERTIES, ZINC-BASE ALLOY

Alloy	Tensile Str., Min. (p.s.i.)	Yield Str., 0.2% offset min. (p.s.i.)	% Elongation, 2", Min.
ZA12	30,000	22,000	6

Note: The above values are presented for reference only — not design. Specific property requirements must be negotiated with the plaster mold casting foundry.

TABLE 4: CHEMICAL COMPOSITION, ZINC-BASE ALLOY

Alloy	Aluminum	Copper	Magnesium	Iron	Zinc
ZA12	11.0-12.5	0.5-1.1	0.01-0.03	0.07	rmdr.

Note: This alloy exhibits excellent castability, ductility, and surface finish.

COPPER-BASE PLASTER MOLD CASTING ALLOYS

Properties and characteristics of some of the copper-base alloys most frequently cast in plaster molds are shown in Tables 5,6, and 7. Aluminum-bronze Alloy CDA955 is frequently used for continuous high-strength, high-impact applications that also require excellent corrosion resistance. This alloy is particularly useful in solving stress corrosion problems because of its excellent corrosion resistance and high level of mechanical properties.

For high conductivity applications requiring electrical conductivity over 80% IACS, Alloy EC801 is often an ideal selection. Plaster mold castings in EC801 provide thin sections, smooth surface finish, fine detail reproduction, and good dimensional tolerances without sacrificing conductivity.

The manganese bronze family of alloys have excellent fluidity and castability, harden to provide exceptionally good wear resistance, and can be used in intermittent high-strength, high-impact applications.

Yellow brass provides excellent machinability, and strength levels equivalent to those of low carbon steels.

Silicon brass has medium-high strength, good ductility, good corrosion resistance, and excellent castability. It is considered an all-purpose alloy, and can be used in stress-corrosion environments.

TABLE 5: MECHANICAL PROPERTIES, COPPER-BASE ALLOYS

Alloy	Temper	Tensile Str., Min. (p.s.i.)	Yield Str., 1.5% exten. under load	% Elongation in 2 in., Min.
Manganese Bronze A, CDA865	AC	65,000	25,000	20
Manganese Bronze B, CDA862	AC	90,000	45,000	18
Manganese Bronze C, CDA63	AC	110,000	60,000	12
Yellow Brass, CDA857	AC	45,000	20,000	25
Silicon Brass, CDA875	AC	65,000	30,000	18
Aluminum Bronze D, CDA955	AC	90,000	40,000	6
Aluminum Bronze D, CDA955	HT	110,000	60,000	3
Electrical Conductivity Copper, CDA801	AC	20,000	—	50

Note: The above properties are provided for reference only — not for design. Specific property levels must be negotiated with the plaster mold foundry.

TABLE 6: CHEMICAL COMPOSITION, COPPER-BASE ALLOYS

Alloy	#863	#862	#865	#857	#875	#955	#801
%							
Tin	0.20	0.20	1.0	0.50-1.5	—	—	—
Lead	0.20	0.20	0.40	0.8-1.5	0.50	—	—
Iron	2.0-4.0	2.0-4.0	0.40-2.0	0.7	—	3.0-5.0	—
Aluminum	5.0-7.5	3.0-4.9	0.50-1.5	0.55	0.50	10.0-11.5	—
Manganese	2.5-5.0	2.5-5.0	0.10-1.5	—	—	3.5	—
Nickel	1.0	1.0	1.0	1.0	—	3.0-5.5	—
Zinc	22.0-28.0	22.0-28.0	36.0-42.0	32.0-40.0	12.0-16.0	—	—
Others, total	—	—	—	—	—	0.50	0.5
Copper	60.0-66.0	60.0-66.0	55.0-60.0	58.0-64.0	79.0 min.	78.0 min.	99.5

Note: Per cents shown are maximum, unless shown as a range or a minimum.

TABLE 7: PROPERTIES SUMMARY, COPPER-BASE ALLOYS

Alloy	#955	#801	Manganese Bronzes	Yellow Brasses	Silicon Brasses
Strength	excellent	fair	good	good	very good
Impact Resistance	excellent	fair	good	good	very good
Wear Resistance	excellent	poor	excellent	poor	very good
Corrosion Resistance	excellent	good	fair	fair	good
Conductivity	fair	excellent	poor	poor	poor
Castability	fair	good	excellent	excellent	excellent
Fluidity	fair	good	excellent	excellent	excellent
Ductility	good	good	fair	good	good
Machinability	fair	fair	good	excellent	good

PRODUCING CAST-TO-SIZE TOOLING WITH THE PLASTER MOLD CASTING PROCESS

GENERAL CONSIDERATIONS

Perhaps one of the most creative applications of the plaster mold casting process has been its use as a method for inexpensive and fast production of special tooling used in the sandcasting and plastics industries.

Matchplate Castings

Plaster-cast matchplate pattern equipment has been commonly used in sandcasting foundries for many decades, as a means for providing accurate, multiple metal patterns for high-production casting jobs. Initially, the sand foundry will make a single-impression wood pattern, from which sample castings for customer approval are made. After the samples have been approved, the sand foundry will send the wood pattern to a plaster mold foundry to have a multiple-impression, aluminum matchplate produced.

Upon receipt of the wood pattern, the matchplate shop will make multiple plaster mold halves, which are precisely positioned and fixed in place in a large, one-piece plaster mold. All of these plaster mold sections are made with conventional metalcasting plasters under the same strict controls described in previous sections of this text.

After drying, the composite, multiple-impression plaster mold halves are assembled for pouring. The final casting, consisting now of several smooth, accurately positioned aluminum impressions, is cleaned and polished before shipment to the sandcasting foundry.

Recent advances in high-pressure sand molding have created an increased demand for solid, heavy-duty pattern equipment, and plaster-cast matchplates have gained widespread acceptance to help meet this need. Traditional use of matchplate patterns for conventional sandcasting foundry production also continues to show strong demand.

Tooling for the Plastic Molding Industry

Over the last two decades, the plastic molding industry has greatly expanded in its importance to various manufacturing and packaging industries. All indications are that this trend will continue, with the "cast-to-size" tooling market growing concurrently.

The plaster mold casting process offers a very attractive method for providing low-cost, quick-turnaround tooling. The process allows for the use of smooth, accurate, and inexpensive wood or plastic models, and as patterns that can be molded and subsequently cast as aluminum or kirksite alloy female molds. These molds are cleaned and polished before being sent to the plastic molder.

Plaster-cast metal molds are presently used for vacuum-forming, rotational molding, compression molding, and limited-run, structural foam molding applications. The same improvements in production technology and controls that have been adopted in recent years by full-production plaster mold casting foundries have been used to expand the capabilities of the tooling shops.

Because of the specialized nature of each "tooling" casting, it is not possible to provide standardized design guidelines for mold castings. We suggest that each "mold" casting be thoroughly discussed with your plaster mold tooling producer, since their versatility and creativity can assist a designer in resolving almost any design question.

PERFORMANCE WITH PLASTER MOLD CASTING

INTRODUCTION

This section features typical examples of precision castings that have been produced through the plaster mold casting process, with examples grouped according to the industry served. Included are electronics, computers, microwave, aircraft/aerospace, optics, and medical. Separate groupings are provided for castings used as prototypes, matchplate tooling, and mold tooling.

The castings shown represent proven performance for a variety of industries, including demanding applications that are not commonly perceived as candidates for the plaster mold casting process. Detail is given on critical inspection and material specifications, other primary design and structural criteria, and dimensions & weights.

In addition, specific aspects of the versatility, advantages, and benefits characteristic of plaster mold casting are noted for each example as appropriate. These include exceptionally smooth surface finish, fine detail reproduction, unusual shapes for castings and their holes/cutouts, thin and intricate sections, sharp or full fillets and corner radii, and flexibility in unit weight, production volume, lead time, and allowance for ongoing design changes.

Numerous additional casting examples, produced for a variety of industries and applications, were not included due to space limitations.

ELECTRONICS

Teleprinter Housing

Close dimensional relationship to case and cover; thin walls with close dimensional control through high-volume production. Inspection to Mil C 6021, Class 3, Grade D. Exceptionally smooth surface. Fine detail reproduction. Unusual shapes for casting and its holes/cutouts. Thin and intricate sections. Sharp fillets/corner radii.

Aluminum-base, A356-T6 (Mil A 21180, Class 10).

20″ x 16″ x 10″; 10 lbs.

Courtesy Atlantic Casting and Engineering Corp.

ELECTRONICS

Airborne Electronic Control Box Housings

.12″ walls with some .25″ ribs. Inspection to Mil C 6021, Class 3, Grade D, 100% x-ray coverage. Various heavy high-stress areas (1-1¼″ x 3″ x 3″ to 2″ x 3″ x 4″) to Grade C. Exceptionally smooth surfaces. Unusual shapes for holes/cutouts.

Aluminum-base, A356-T6 (QQA 601).

20″ x 25″ x 33″; 86 lbs. and 68 lbs.

Courtesy Jacob Casting Div., Jacob Pattern Works Inc.

ELECTRONICS

Electronic Control System Housing

Intricate sections; wall thickness range .125-.440″. Inspection to Grade C. Exceptionally smooth surface.

Aluminum-base, A356-T6 (AMS4218)

8″ x 9″ x 4½″, 3¼ lbs.

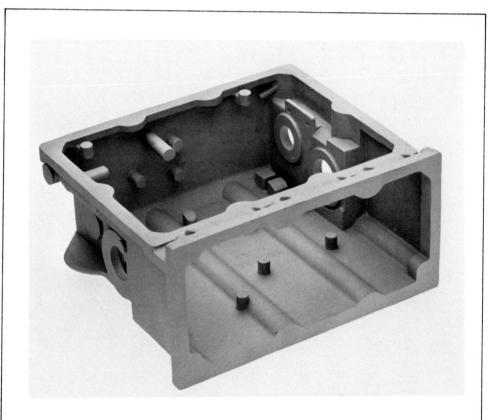

Courtesy Supreme Castings & Pattern Co.

ELECTRONICS

Electronic Control System Multiple Module Holder

.040 ±.010 on module septums. Septum depth, 4″; width, 6″. Inspection to MIL C 6021, Class 1, Grade C. Exceptionally smooth surface. Fine detail reproduction. Unusual shape for casting and holes/cutouts. Thin and intricate sections. Both sharp and full fillets and corners.

Aluminum-base, A356-T61 (MIL A 21180, Class 10)

34″ x 4″ x 7″, 10 lbs.

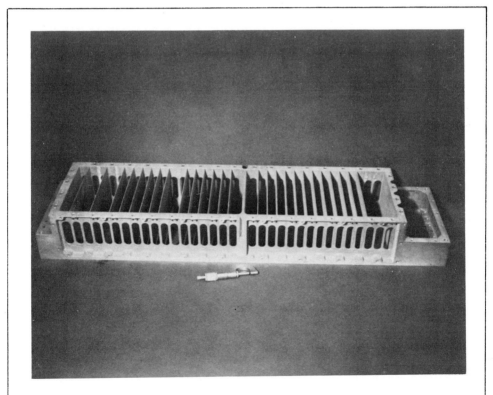

Courtesy Sims Castings Corp.

ELECTRONICS

System Component Housing

Thin, thick, and intricate sections; wall thickness range
.065-.750". Inspection to MIL C 6021, Class 1B, Grade C. Exceptionally smooth surface. Fine detail reproduction.
Unusual shapes for casting and its holes/cutouts. Both sharp
and full fillets and corners.

Aluminum-base, A356-T61 (MIL A 21180, Class 10).

12" x 10", 10 lbs.

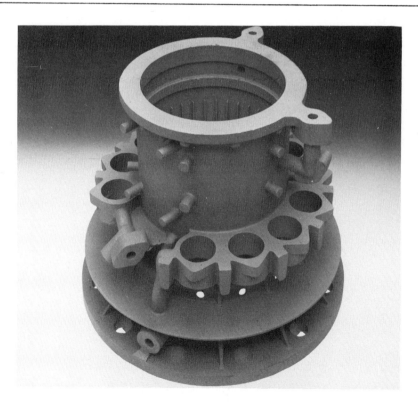

Courtesy Supreme Castings & Pattern Co.

ELECTRONICS

Radio System Heat Sink

.060" fins generated off 3/8" thick base to utilize the 90% IACS conductivity offered by alloy to achieve maximum heat dissipation in smallest possible space. Exceptionally smooth surface finish. Fine detail reproduction. Thin sections.

Copper-base, EC 801.

6" x 4" x 5/8"; 4 lbs.

Courtesy Atlantic Casting and Engineering Corp.

ELECTRONICS

Electronic Flight Gear Housing/Heat Sink

Thin and intricate sections; wall thickness range .065-.250″. Meet Inspection Grade C. Exceptionally smooth surface. Fine detail reproduction. Unusual shapes for casting and its holes/cutouts. Sharp fillets and corners.

Aluminum-base, A356-T6 (QQA601.)

20″ x 4½″ x 6½″, 6 lbs.

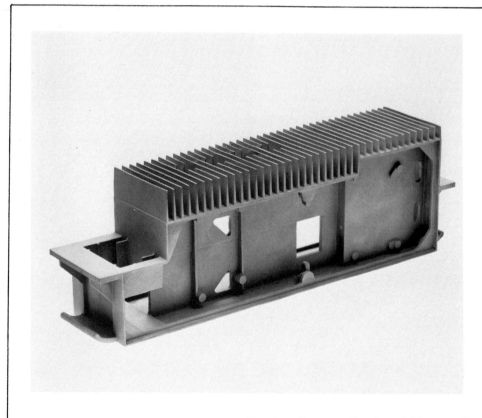

Courtesy Supreme Castings & Pattern Co.

COMPUTER

Peripheral Drive Housing

Produce medium/high volume in a short period. Fast tooling. Allow for ease in making ongoing design changes. Exceptionally smooth surface. Simulated diecasting application.

Aluminum-base, A356-T6 (QQA 601).

14″ x 12″ x 4″; 4.5 lbs.

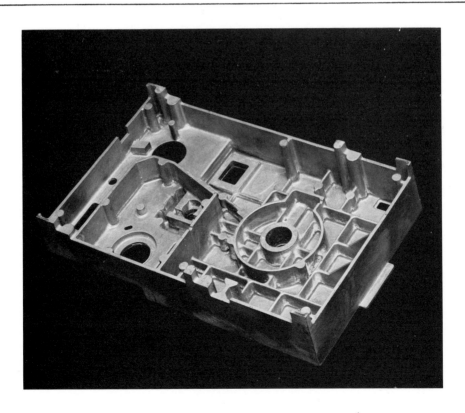

Courtesy Atlantic Casting and Engineering Corp.

COMPUTER

Airborne Computer Electronics Housing

High material integrity in thin-wall, dimensionally-stable casting. Inspection to Mil C 6021, Class 3, Grade C. Exceptionally smooth surface. Unusual shapes for holes/cutouts. Thin and intricate sections. Sharp fillets/corner radii.

Aluminum-base, A356-T6 (AMS 4260).

8" x 8" x 1"; 1 lb.

Courtesy Atlantic Casting and Engineering Corp.

COMPUTER

Computer System Keyboard Display Module

No draft for card guides in center. Close tolerances on wall perpendicularity and parallelism, and also on holes/cutouts. Exceptionally smooth surface. Unusual casting shape. Thin and intricate sections.

Aluminum-base, A356-T51.

27″ x 22″ x 20″, 28 lbs.

Courtesy Accurate Mold Co.

MICROWAVE

Radar Antenna Heat Sink

2500 no-draft pins, 1/8" diameter x 1½" deep; no radii at base of pins. Casting machined complete, plated, and painted. High-volume production; 2,000 units completed, 5,000 planned total. Exceptionally smooth surface. Fine detail reproduction. Unusual casting shape. Sharp fillets and corner radii.

Aluminum-base, #356-T51 (QQA601).

31" x 8" x 2½", 7 lbs.

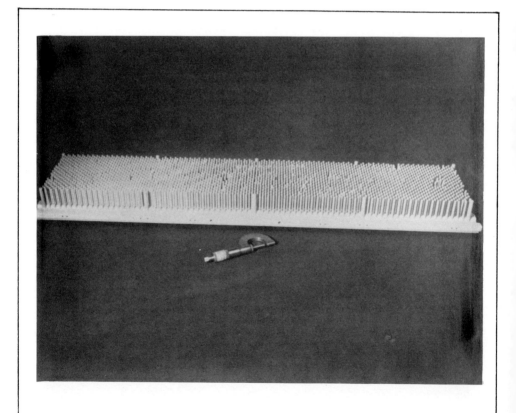

Courtesy Sims Castings Corp.

MICROWAVE

Phased-Array Antenna Element

Inspection to Mil C 6021, Class 4, Grade D for antenna elements; to Mil C 6021, Class 4, Grade C for base. Close dimensional control and high casting integrity through run of 25,000. Intricate shapes for casting and its holes. Exceptionally smooth surface finish.

Aluminum-base, A356-T6 (Mil C 11886).

6″ x 6″ x 10″; 2½ lbs.

Courtesy Atlantic Casting and Engineering Corp.

MICROWAVE

Radar Unit Heat Sinks

Replacements for similar-size parts formerly assembled from 5 to 9 small castings via machining with tongue and groove joints and riveting together. Inspection to Mil C 6021, Class 4, Grade D. Casting in one piece to gain manufacturing economies, higher strength, and higher heat transfer efficiency. Approx. 4500 pins 1/8″ diameter x 1½″ long on a ½″-thick base.

Aluminum-base, A356-T51 (QQA 601).
14″ x 24″, 42 lbs.; 14″ x 40″, 60 lbs.

Courtesy Jacob Casting Div., Jacob Pattern Works Inc.

MICROWAVE

Radar Antenna Waveguide

Close tolerance, ±.003″ to 1″, 63 microinches inside surface finish, double iris-machined complete. Exceptionally smooth surface. Fine detail reproduction. Unusual shape for casting and its holes/cutouts. Thin and intricate sections. Sharp fillets and corner radii.

Aluminum-base, #356-T51, QQA601 (D712.0).

11″ x 4″ x 3″, 2 lbs.

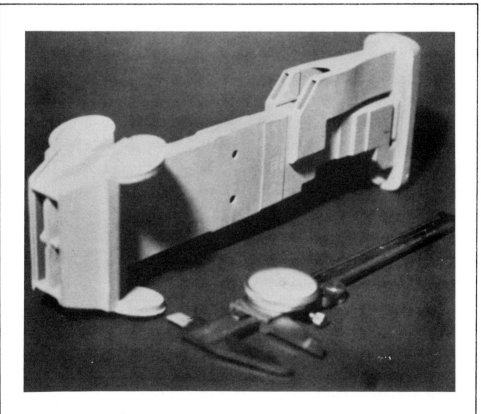

Courtesy Sims Castings Corp.

AIRCRAFT/AEROSPACE

Aircraft Fuel System Boost Pump Housing

Close dimensional tolerances. Inspection to Mil C 6021, Class 2A, Grade B. Exceptionally smooth surface. Unusual shapes for casting and its holes/cutouts. Thin and intricate sections.

Aluminum-base, A356-T6 (Mil A 21180, Class 12).

8″ x 12″; 5¼ lbs.

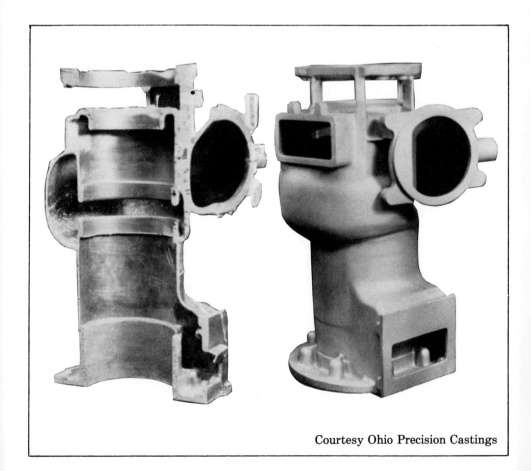

Courtesy Ohio Precision Castings

AIRCRAFT/AEROSPACE

Airborne Temperature Regulator Plenum Casting

Fourteen separate cores required to make chambers and intricate wire passages. Inspection to Mil C 6021, Class 3, Grades C and D. Exceptionally smooth surface. Fine detail reproduction. Unusual shapes for casting and its holes/cutouts. Intricate cored passageways and thin sections.

Aluminum-base, A356-T6 (QQA 601).

30″ x 26″ x 9″; 28 lbs.

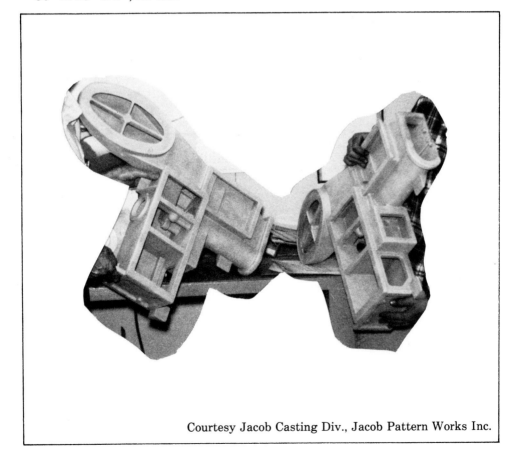

Courtesy Jacob Casting Div., Jacob Pattern Works Inc.

AIRCRAFT/AEROSPACE

Fuselage Component

Close dimensional control. Inspection to Mil C 6021, Class 1 Grade C. Meet demanding mechanical properties, with test specimens excised directly from castings. Exceptionally smooth surface. Unusual and intricate casting shape. Sharp fillets and corner radii.

Aluminum-base, A356-T6 (Mil A 21180, Class 10).

18″ x 23″ x 6″; 7.5 lbs.

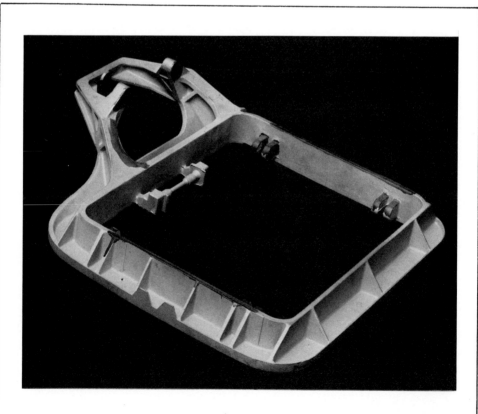

Courtesy Atlantic Casting and Engineering Corp.

AIRCRAFT/AEROSPACE

Aircraft Fuel System Inlet Pump Housing

Close dimensional tolerances. Inspection to Mil C 6021, Class 2A, Grade B. Exceptionally smooth surface. Fine detail reproduction. Unusual shapes for casting and its holes/cutouts. Thin and intricate sections.

Aluminum-base, A356-T6 (Mil A 21180, Class 12).

4″ x 8″; 2¼ lbs.

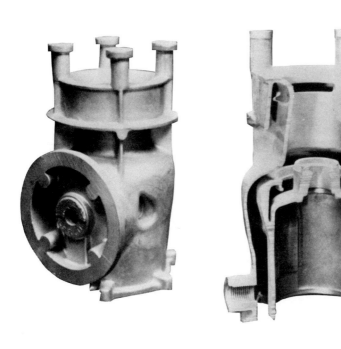

Courtesy Ohio Precision Castings

OPTICS

Infrared Telescope Housing

Good dimensional stability. Freedom from internal draft. Exceptionally smooth surface. Fine detail reproduction. Unusual shapes for casting and its holes/cutouts. Thin and intricate sections. Sharp fillets and corner radii.

Aluminum-base, #356-T6 (AMS 4260).

14″ diameter x 18″ long, 8 lbs.

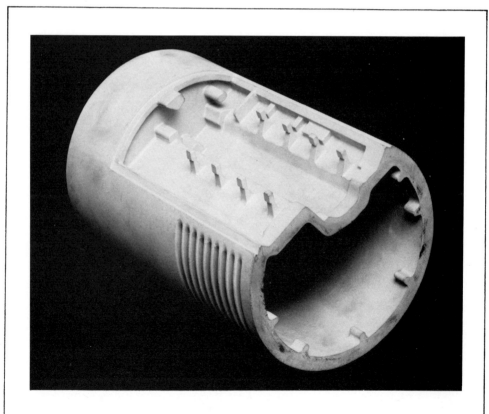

Courtesy Atlantic Casting and Engineering Corp.

OPTICS

Optical Reader Housing

Dimensional stability and casting soundness during and after machining. Freedom from porosity. Unusual casting shape. Both sharp and full fillets/corners.

Aluminum-base, A356-T71.

10" x 7" x 7"; 4 lbs.

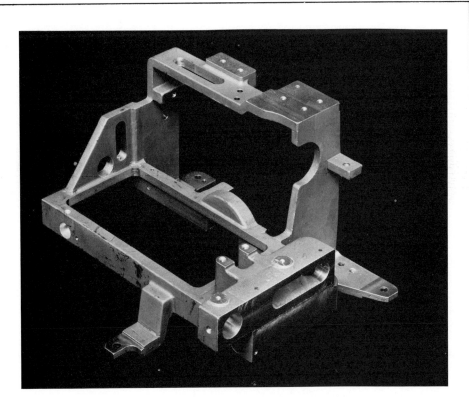

Courtesy Atlantic Casting and Engineering Corp.

MEDICAL

Dermatology Surgical Instrument Housing

Exceptionally smooth surface, freedom from porosity after plating, and close dimensional control to allow for direct contact with human tissue during surgery. Unusual shapes for casting and its holes/cutouts.

Cooper-base, manganese bronze per CDA 863.

6″ x 4″ x 4″; 4.8 lbs.

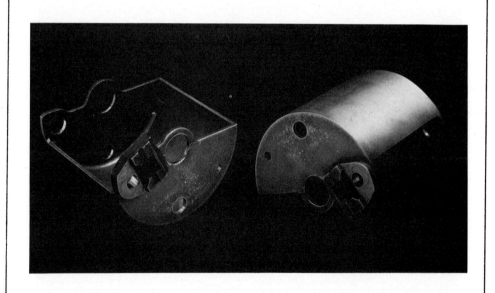

Courtesy Atlantic Casting and Engineering Corp.

MEDICAL

Medical Test Equipment Bezel

.080" wall thickness. Low tool cost for cosmetically-appealing part in low-volume production. Exceptionally smooth surface. Fine detail reproduction. Unusual shapes for holes/cutouts. Thin and intricate sections. Sharp fillets/corner radii.

Aluminum-base, #356-T51.

15" x 4" x 3"; 1 lb.

Courtesy Atlantic Casting and Engineering Corp.

PROTOTYPES

Automotive Fan Shroud Diecasting Prototype

Porosity-free. Close tolerances, within .005-.010 overall. Exceptionally smooth surface. Fine detail reproduction. Thin sections.

Aluminum-base, #308.

6 x 5″ x 1½″, ¾ lb.

Courtesy Kuhlman Casting Company

PROTOTYPES

Automotive Emission Control Housing Diecasting Prototype

Thin and intricate sections. Exceptionally smooth surface. Unusual shapes for casting and its holes/cutouts.

Zinc-base, ILZRO-12.

3″ x 3″ x 2½″; 0.8 lbs.

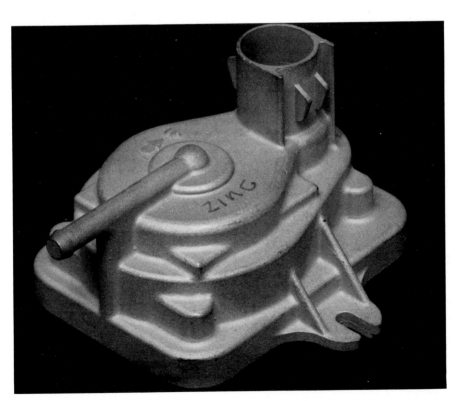

Courtesy Atlantic Casting and Engineering Corp.

PROTOTYPES

Automotive Oil Pan Diecasting Prototype

±.005 general dimensional tolerance. Porosity-free.

Aluminum-base, #356-T6.

18″ x 10″ x 13″; 7 lbs.

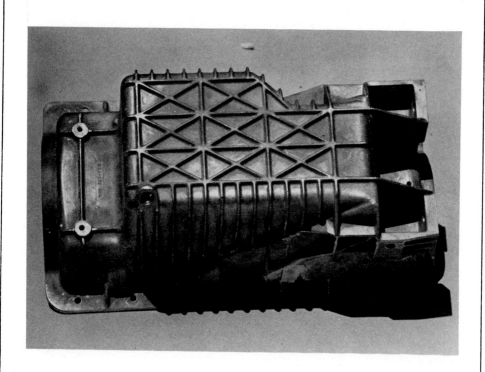

Courtesy Seaport Mold & Casting Co.

PROTOTYPES

Radio Housing Diecasting Prototype

Fast tooling turnaround, with ability to make design changes without affecting tool life during high-volume production. Exceptionally smooth surface; also stylized surface. Fine detail reproduction. Unusual shape for casting and its holes/cutouts. Thin and intricate sections. Sharp fillets/corner radii.

Zinc-base, ILZRO-12.

7" x 7" x 1½"; 1.3 lb.

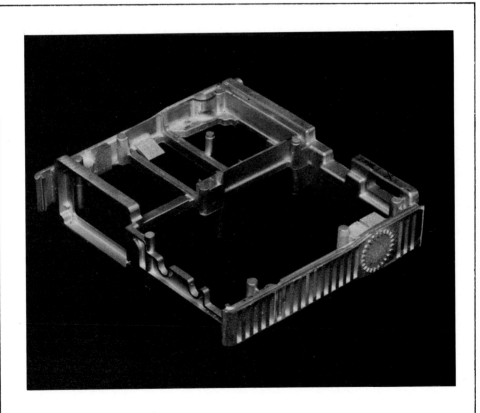

Courtesy Atlantic Casting and Engineering Corp.

PROTOTYPES

Printed Circuit Card Holder Diecasting Prototype

Quick turnaround & preproduction. Close dimensional control: ±.015″ over 10″ length. Exceptionally smooth surface. Thin and intricate sections. Sharp fillets/corner radii.

Aluminum-base, #356-T6.

20″ x 12″ x ½″; 1 lb.

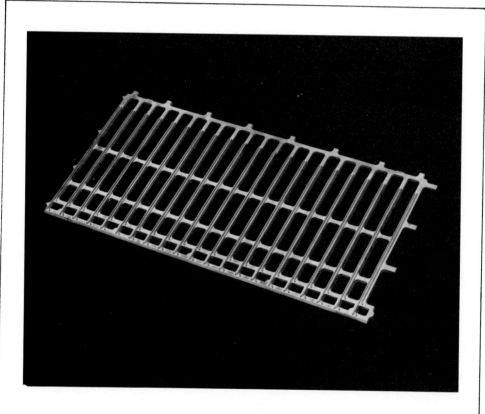

Courtesy Atlantic Casting and Engineering Corp.

PROTOTYPES

Electrical Housing Diecasting Prototype

Cast 4 separate parts for matching into one unit via plastic inserts. ±.005 general dimensional tolerance.

Zinc-base, ILZRO-12.

Each part approx. 3½″ x 1½″ x 1″; total 3/4 lb.

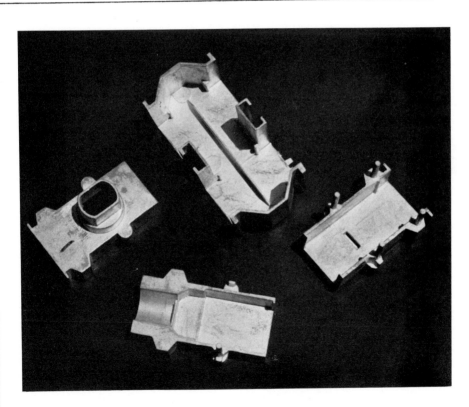

Courtesy Bay State Cast Products Inc.

TOOLING: MATCHPLATE

Pressure-Cast Matchplate
For Automatic Molding Machine (Non Ferrous)

±.005 mismatch/plate shift tolerance; .004″ draft allowed in pattern.

Aluminum-base, special combination.

Flask size, 14″ x 19″. 30 lbs.

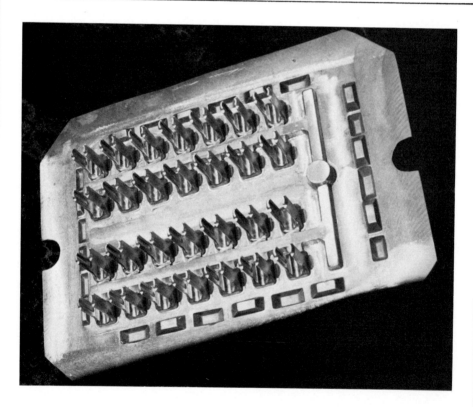

Courtesy Bay State Cast Products Inc.

TOOLING: MATCHPLATE

**Pressure-Cast Matchplate For
Automatic Molding Machine (Ferrous)**

±.015 general dimensional tolerance. No plate shift/mismatch. Porosity-free.
Material Specification

Aluminum-base, #319.

Dimensions & Weight

Flask size, 14" x 19". 28 lbs.

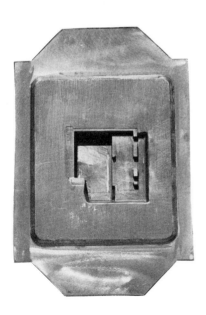

Courtesy Seaport Mold & Casting Co.

TOOLING: MOLD

Aircraft Inner Panel Mold

Tolerances within .030. Exceptionally smooth surface. Cooling lines cast in mold. Injection-molded to AID parts.

Zinc-base, Kirksite.

35″ x 30″ x 8″, 1900 lbs.

Courtesy Kuhlman Casting Company

TOOLING: MOLD

Food Packaging Mold

9-cavity mold for expandable polystyrene packaging, made from single model of actual part. Unusual shapes for casting and its holes/cutouts. Exceptionally smooth surface. Fine detail reproduction. Both sharp and full fillets and corners. High unit weight.

Aluminum-base special, combination of A319 and A343.

39″ x 48″ x 4″, 248 lbs.

Courtesy Plaster Process Castings Co.

TOOLING: MOLD

Foam-Rubber Basketball Mold

Textured surface. Absolute spherical uniformity.

Aluminum-base, #319.

7″ I.D.; 4.5 lbs.

Courtesy Seaport Mold & Casting Co.

TOOLING: MOLD

Plastic Figurine Mold

Matching irregular parting line. Smooth cavities. Fine detail reproduction.

Aluminum-base, #356.

28″ x 38″; 200 lbs.

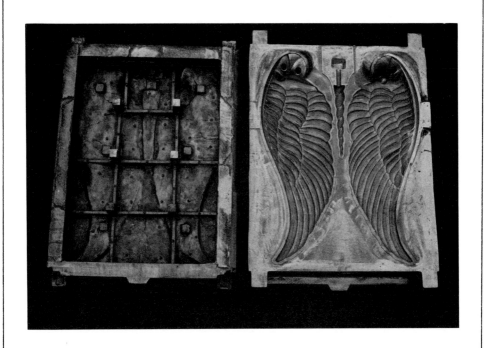

Courtesy Bay State Cast Products Inc.

TOOLING: MOLD

Engine Paint Mask Mold

7-up mold made from single pattern. Undercuts required making rubber patterns off of master. Stainless steel cooling tubes cast in mold. Exceptionally smooth surface. Fine detail reproduction. Unusual shapes for casting and its holes/cutouts. Both sharp and full fillets and corners.

Aluminum-base special, combination of A319 and A343.

22″ x 23″ x 5″, 56 lbs.

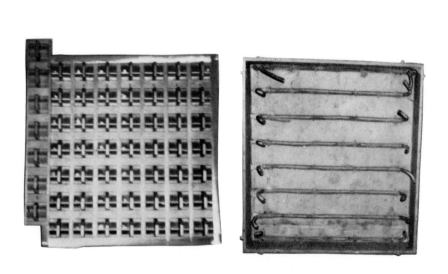

Courtesy Plaster Process Castings Co.

INDEX